What Do Pigs Dream About?

Written by **Kelsey Bonham & Shelley Sleeper**   Illustrated by **Shane Burke**

Dedicated to my parents. Thanks for always
encouraging me to follow my dreams.
-KB

Dedicated to Mommom. Thank you for your
unconditional love and support.
-SS

Dedicated to Hunter, Mallory, and Harrison.
-SB

shelleysleeper.com

Graphic Design by Francisco Macias O

Published by Aviva Publishing New York

Printed by Sunrise Design & Printing Co.

18 17 16 15 14 13   10 9 8 7 6 5 4 3 2 1

Pigs might dream about...

proving to the world, they can really fly.

teaching the animals how to be safe on the farm.

having legs like a giraffe so they can reach the fresh, crisp apples.

Pigs might dream about...

the day the Veggsicle Truck stops at the farm.

10

Pigs might dream about...

11

building up the courage to stand up to the wolf.

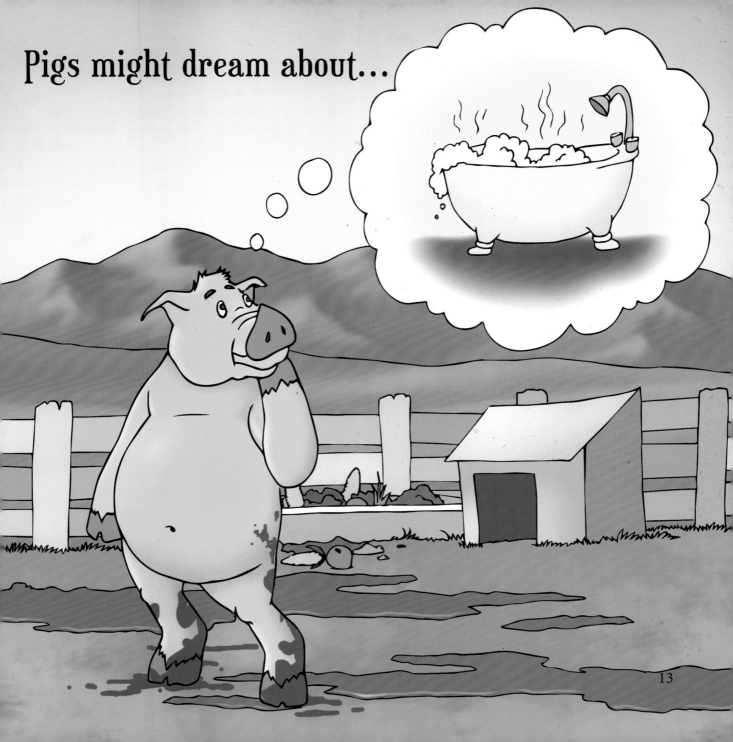

scrubbing away the mud and muck in a steaming, hot bubble bath.

Pigs might dream about...

15

building up the endurance to be
the fastest animal on the farm.

Pigs might dream about...

CATS	FARMS	PONDS	PIGS	COWS	CHICKENS
$100	$100	$100	$100	$100	$100
$200	$200	$200	$200	$200	$200
$300	$300	$300	$300	$300	$300
$400	$400	$400	$400	$400	$400
$500	$500		$500		

$2500 $18000 $4500

Rocco Pierre Callie

taking home the grand prize in the Farmyard Knowledge Bowl.

finally scratching
that hard to reach itch!

Pigs might dream about...

how thrilling it would be
to spin a web.

But most likely, they dream about...

a wolf-free life!

FUN FACTS ABOUT PIGS

- There are around 2 billion pigs in the world.

- Pigs are omnivores; they consume both plants and animals.

- A baby pig is called a piglet, an adult female is called a sow, and an adult male is called a boar.

- Pigs have four toes on each hoof but walk on just two toes. This makes it look like they are walking on their tiptoes.

- Pigs do not have sweat glands. To cool themselves they roll in the mud.

- Pork, bacon and ham come from pigs.

- Pigs are mainly active at night.

- Pigs are highly social and intelligent animals.

- Pigs recognize their names and frequently come when called.

- Some people like to keep pigs as pets.

- The pig is a litter-bearing animal.

- A typical female will give birth to ten or more piglets, twice a year.

- Pigs have an excellent sense of smell.

- Pigs use their snouts to find food in the ground.

- Pigs are not dirty animals. Given the opportunity, they will remain extremely clean.